COLIN WHITTOCK

THE PERILS OF MOTORING

CENTURY
LONDON SYDNEY AUCKLAND JOHANNESBURG

By the same author

The Perils of Pushing 40
The Perils of Moving House
The Perils of Parenthood
The Perils of Getting Married

Copyright © Colin Whittock 1989

First published in 1989 by Random Century Ltd,
20 Vauxhall Bridge Road,
London SW1V 2SA

Random Century Australia Pty Ltd, 20 Alfred Street,
Milsons Point, Sydney 2061, Australia

Random Century New Zealand Ltd, PO Box 40–086,
Glenfield, Auckland 10, New Zealand

Century Hutchinson South African Pty Ltd, PO Box 337,
Bergvlei, 2012 South Africa

Reprinted 1990

British Library Cataloguing in Publication Data
Whittock, Colin
The perils of motoring.
English humorous cartoons. Collections from
individual artists
I. Title
741.5'942

ISBN 0–7126–3526–2

Filmset by Deltatype, Ellesmere Port
Printed in Great Britain by Richard Clay Ltd, Bungay, Suffolk

Choosing A Car

When choosing a new car we look for the design we like . . .

I don't really mind as long as it impresses the neighbours.

the colour . . .

The salesman let me have it as a special favour – apparently they only made twelve puce models!

the performance . . .

Never mind 0–60 mph in seven seconds – it takes him longer than that to put on his seat-belt.

A minibus might be better.

the image.

Grow-up!

Some dealers are more honest than others. . .

It was driven by a dear old lady on Sunday mornings – in rally cross events!

but you can never be certain.

We don't think of it as 'going round the clock twice', sir, simply as 'well run-in'.

Sometimes you decide to sell your car privately . . .

I'm only protecting you against the Trade Descriptions Act.

but you must be careful of callers . . .

He seemed a nice chap, asked if he could take it for a run around the block . . . about an hour ago!

When buying a new car, salesmen are really helpful.

It really suits sir!

They make you feel important

Frankly, sir, I couldn't sell this car to just anybody.

and treat you like old friends . . .

*I couldn't sleep soundly tonight if I let you
resist this magnificent offer!*

with every courtesy . . .

Perhaps your daughter would like to try . . .
oh, your wife!

until the sale has been made and you report a fault.

That's nothing to do with me, see the Service Department, Mr . . . er . . . er . . .

Second-hand car salesmen are a different breed again . . .

Whatever you want, I've got it or can get it.

*That's the basic, but you can have optional
extras like wheels and engines.*

and always ready to do a favour.

*It's really my partner's car, but if you want
it, I'll sell it to you before he comes back!*

Some are called sharks . . .

We're tidying up the bodywork now, sir.

and sail close to the wind .

*At the moment, sir, we have red, blue,
green or black escorts in stock.*

Learning To Drive

Some people are taught by relatives.

The difficulty is trying to teach him everything he thinks he knows.

Others prefer a recommended driving instructor . . .

Are you sure he's good?

but eventually we pass our test, and begin to learn to drive.

I did it! I passed my test, aren't you going to congratulate me?

City Driving

City motoring is fast . . .

Will somebody let us in? – I'm not sure that I want to be 'let in'!

in a foul atmosphere . . .

Personally I can't wait for the new laws on exhaust emissions!

and unless you know the lane system . . .

That's where we need to be.

it can mean several circuits before one reaches one's destination.

We'd better get it right soon or I'll run out of petrol!

Then having reached one's destination, parking is a problem .

I told you we should have come by train!

Some cities have meter zones . . .

Hurry up and fetch the car, I've found a space.

with ever-vigilant traffic wardens .

Very droll, gentlemen!

Some have expensive multi-storey car parks . . .

Don't worry, sir, we'll find your car.

and others have open-air 'Pay and Display' zones.

Country Motoring

Some can remember the days when one could cruise, unpressured, along rolling country lanes.

Nowadays it can still happen, but one finds congestion quickly builds up.

Never mind we'll be turning left in a minute.

Quaint features still exist . . .

I didn't notice, probably out of date anyway.

that we're no longer generally accustomed to.

*So much for your 'it's been very dry lately,
there'll be nothing in it'.*

But a country drive can still be a joy . . .

so long as you don't break down.

We can get miles from anywhere . . .

Apparently, we're 75 miles away from the nearest cash dispenser.

though not always as far away from some things as we'd like.

Drink your tea then, and we'll press on.

Motorway Motoring

Motorways mean we can drive quickly to most parts of the country . . .

I believe the scenery around here is lovely.

except around London.

*The M25 must be the nearest thing to being
lost in space.*

There are roadworks . . .

Then, when that lane has been repaired, this one will have worn out.

and eight lane motorways are now planned.

Think of it as more freedom not just thousands of miles of more roadworks.

Motorists turn into motorway types – the overtaking lane speedster . . .

If I'm doing 75 mph, what must he be doing?

the fast-lane fogey . . .

the inside-lane snail . . .

and the lorry driver.

Touring

Packing the car for a touring holiday has to be planned.

I knew I'd forgotten something!

Extra spares are wise especially if going to remote areas.

Oh, all right, if you're going to moan all the time, I'll see if I can get the spares into the trailer!

Good road maps are essential . . .

and a good navigator.

We should have taken that last turning on the left.

Too long a distance between each stage should be avoided . . .

We should be in Oban for breakfast.

. . . though not too short.

Some like the hardy under-canvas life . . .

and use trailers.

You were supposed to hook it on 50 miles ago.

Ferries can be fun . . .

Missed . . . laddie!

although it is always wise to check tide tables.

Touring abroad is a different joy.

One can enjoy the intricacies of foreign driving . . .

No, it's my fault, I should have stopped on green.

where attitudes to bumps may not be quite the same.

'Petite' – *what does he mean!*

Even though we carry spares, expert help is sometimes needed . . .

Avez-vous un 'big-end' pour un . . . ?

and with directions.

Finally on the return journey we can take advantage of the duty free

60 litres of beer each, did you say?

Accidents

It's a lucky driver who has never had an accident.

Some are devastatingly silly.

You know I said I'd put your car in the garage, dad, – I missed!

Some absolutely straightforward.

I didn't think you'd stop on red.

But it's never your fault.

Insurance details have to be exchanged . . .

Insurance details. What are they?

and witnesses found . . . if there are any . . .

A diagram of the accident has to be sent in . . .

and eventually an estimate is obtained.

On insurance? – ok, I'll double it for luck.

Servicing

In order to keep your car in good condition, servicing is essential.

I'm loathe to take it in, it's running beautifully!

We can be pleasantly surprised.

I only said, 'It's part of the service, no charge'.

Some experts prefer to service their own . . .

to their own advantage . . .

I bet he's in the pub again.

which can be risky . . .

*I might have known, he only serviced it
yesterday!*

but satisfying.

I've saved £80 and I've got a few bits left over!

Some garages are reasonable . . .

*They're about the best around here, they
keep their over-charging to a minimum.*

He didn't stagger and go pale – you must have missed something.

MOT's can be a worry . . .

*Good grief! Is your MOT due again already,
Mr Grotley?*

especially if a lot needs attention.

It's not all bad, your cigarette lighter works!

Offences

We are all likely at some time to be apprehended for committing an offence, whether it's for speeding . . .

Slow down, dad – the policeman on the motorbike can't get past!

I love the way they brake when they spot us.

or for illegal parking . . .

*You'd have only booked me if I'd parked on
double yellow lines!*

or being without tax or MOT . . .

Jackpot, sir!

or for dangerous driving . . .

or drinking and driving.

Which of the three tubes do you want me to blow in?

Magistrates are now toughening up on offenders.

Good grief – the black cap!

Accessories

Car phones are becoming popular . . .

*Hold on mother, we seem to have stopped
for some reason.*

Wonderful sound systems are now available . . .

There's nothing quite like driving through the Malverns with a spot of Elgar on the quadraphonic . . . !

with amazing reception.

Would you mind turning that down please?

Heated seats.

*Toast? Oh no, I left my sandwiches in my
back pocket!*

Boot spoilers.

I haven't a clue what it does, but it looks good . . .

Efficient heating systems.

*I see what you mean, the heating system is
very good!*

A company car can be a marvellous asset . . .

. . . and there's your new company car the other side of mine – it's a Metro.

for some.

*It's the other twelve months of the year I
find embarrassing.*

Personalised number plates can also appeal

*I tried to buy him one for his birthday but
TW1T wasn't available.*

**We can join clubs to ensure the attention
of experts.**

*I suppose you'll just touch something and it
will start straightaway.*

But eventually our beloved goes the way of most things.

This old Marina – did you notice a pair of knitting needles in the glove compartment?